Supporting
Phonics
and
Spelling

FOR AGES 6–7

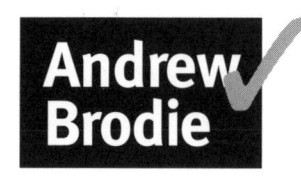

Andrew
Brodie

Contents

Andrew Brodie: Supporting Phonics & Spelling © A & C Black Publishers Ltd. 2006

Introduction

Supporting Phonics and Spelling is aimed at children in mainstream classrooms who have been identified as needing 'additional' or 'different' literacy support, particularly in phonics and spelling. The activities can be used by anyone working with children who fall into this category, whether you are a teacher, classroom assistant or parent.

Typically the six to seven year-old children for whom the book is intended will be working at the levels expected of Reception or Year 1 children or may simply need extra help in tackling the level of work appropriate for Year 2. Their difficulties may be short-term, and could be overcome with extra practice and support on a one-to-one or small group basis, or they may be long-term, where such support enables them to make progress but at a level behind their peer group. The activities in this book provide exactly what these children need – systematic repetition and practice of early phonic skills, based on a strong foundation of synthetic phonics and the best features of analytic phonics. The *Supporting Phonics and Spelling* series reflects the best practice in teaching spelling through phonics. It provides an approach that is:

- Systematic
- Multi-sensory
- Based on speaking and listening
- Linked closely to reading skills

This book is organised into three-page sets. It is vital that the teaching assistant or class teacher reads the 'Teacher's notes' on 'Sheet a' before starting the lesson. This first page in each set introduces specific phonemes and provides a good opportunity for the teacher and child to sound them out together. Children can also use their multi-sensory skills at this stage by drawing the letters in sand or making them out of dough or modelling clay. The second worksheet revises the same phonemes, but with a particular emphasis on speaking, listening and writing. The final worksheet in the set features a list of words containing the phonemes for further practice and consolidation. When used together, the three worksheets provide a thorough grounding in the phonic knowledge and skills that children need for confident reading, writing and spelling.

All the worksheets can be used on their own or alongside other literacy schemes that are already established within your school. The activities are simple and self-explanatory and the instruction text is deliberately kept to a minimum to make the pages easy to use for adults and less daunting for children to follow.

We recommend that the children use the *Supporting Phonics and Spelling* worksheets on a daily basis for approximately 20 minutes. Regular practice of previous learning is an integral part of the series. In completing the activities, teachers should place particular emphasis on speaking and listening skills.

Children generally achieve the greatest success in an atmosphere of support and encouragement. Praise from a caring adult can be the best reward for the children's efforts. The worksheets and activities in this book will provide many opportunities for children to enjoy these successes. The development of a positive attitude and the resulting increase in self-esteem will help them with all of their schoolwork.

Definitions and explanations of terms

(Please note that some publications will give slightly different definitions.)

Phoneme
A phoneme is a unit of sound and can be represented by:
one letter e.g. /b/ as in **b**at   two letters e.g. /ee/ as in sw**ee**t
three letters e.g. /ear/ as in n**ear**
Note that a phoneme can be represented in several different ways
e.g. the sound /ee/ can be represented by:

ee as in f**ee**t	**ei** as in c**ei**ling	**ie** as in ch**ie**f
ea as in n**ea**t	**i** as in sk**i**	**e_e** as in P**e**t**e**

Vowel phoneme
A vowel phoneme makes an open sound and always contains at least one vowel – you usually have to open your mouth to say it.
Examples of vowel phonemes are:

/a/ as in b**a**t	/ie/ as in cr**ie**s	/oo/ as in b**oo**k
/ur/ as in t**ur**n	/ow/ as in t**ow**n	

Consonant phoneme
A consonant phoneme always contains at least one consonant and usually involves closing the mouth, 'biting' the lower lip, or touching the roof of the mouth with the tongue. (There are exceptions e.g. /h/). Examples of consonant phonemes are:

/b/ as in **b**at	/f/ as in **ph**otograph
/th/ as in **th**ey	/ng/ as in si**ng**

Grapheme
A grapheme is a letter, a pair of letters or a group of letters representing a single sound e.g. **ee**, **ei**, **ie**, **ea**, **i** and **e_e** are all graphemes representing the sound /ee/.

Grapheme/phoneme correspondence
The relationship between letters and the sounds that they represent.

Digraph
A digraph consists of two letters representing a single sound. So, for example, the grapheme **ch** is a consonant digraph because it is made up of two consonants. The grapheme **ee** is a vowel digraph and although it contains a consonant, **ow** is also a vowel digraph, because it makes an open sound like a vowel does.

Split digraph
A split digraph consists of two vowels separated by a consonant to make one phoneme e.g.   **e_e** as in P**e**t**e**   **i_e** as in m**i**n**e**   **a_e** as in c**a**m**e**

Trigraph
A trigraph is a group of three letters representing a single sound.
The vowel phonemes /air/ and /ear/ are trigraphs.

Cluster
A cluster consists of two or more letters making more than one sound. For example:
t   h   r   are three letters that can make the cluster **thr**, which consists of the phonemes /th/ and /r/.

Blending
Blending is the process of combining different sounds (phonemes) to be able to say a particular word or to make up part of a word e.g.
/sh/   /i/   /p/   can be blended to make the word ship.

/th/   /r/   are blended to make the cluster **thr**. Sometimes a cluster like this will be called a blend.

Segmenting
Segmenting is the process of splitting a word into its different phonemes to be able to spell it e.g. **ship** can be segmented into the three phonemes /sh/ /i/ /p/.

Onset and rime
The terms 'onset' and 'rime' are used together when analysing words. For example, in the word 'cat' the phoneme represented by the letter 'c' is described as the onset and the final cluster 'at' is described as the rime. Note that words that end with a particular rime always rhyme but words that rhyme do not always contain the same rime! For example, cat, rat and bat all end with the rime 'at' and all rhyme. But the words tough and muff rhyme but have the rimes 'ough' and 'uff'.

vc
vowel/consonant e.g. the word *it*

cv
consonant/vowel e.g. the word *be*

cvc
consonant/vowel/consonant e.g. the word *cat*

ccvc
consonant/consonant/vowel/consonant e.g. the word *shop*

cvcc
consonant/vowel/consonant/consonant e.g. the word *fast*

Andrew Brodie: Supporting Phonics & Spelling © A & C Black Publishers Ltd. 2006

An introduction to phonemes

Language can be analysed by considering the separate sounds that combine to make up spoken words. These sounds are called phonemes and the English language has more than forty of them. It is possible to concentrate on forty-two main phonemes but here we list forty-four phonemes including those that are commonly used only in some regions of the country.

It is helpful to look at each phoneme individually and then at some sample words that demonstrate how the phoneme is represented by different graphemes as shown in the list below. Try reading each word out loud to spot the phoneme in each one. For the simple vowel sounds the graphemes are shown in bold text.

Vowel phonemes	Sample words
/a/	b**a**t
/e/	l**e**g, gu**e**ss, h**ea**d, s**ai**d, s**ay**s
/i/	b**i**g, plant**e**d, b**u**sy, cr**y**stal, d**e**cide, **e**xact, g**u**ilt, r**e**peat
/o/	d**o**g, **ho**nest, w**a**s, qu**a**rrel, tr**ou**gh, v**au**lt, y**ach**t (the ch is silent)
/u/	b**u**g, l**o**ve, bl**oo**d, c**o**mfort, r**ou**gh, y**ou**ng
/ae/	rain, day, game, navy, weigh, they, great, rein
/ee/	been, team, field, these, he, key, litre, quay, suite
/ie/	pie, high, sign, my, bite, child, guide, guy, haiku
/oe/	boat, goes, crow, cone, gold, sew
/ue/	soon, do, July, blue, chew, June, bruise, shoe, you, move, through
/oo/	book, put
/ar/	barn, bath (regional), laugh (regional), baa, half, clerk, heart, guard
/ur/	Thursday, girl, her, learn, word
/or/	born, door, warm, all, draw, cause, talk, aboard, abroad, before, four, bought, taught
/ow/	brown, found, plough
/oi/	join, toy, buoy
/air/	chair, pear, care, where, their, prayer
/ear/	near, cheer, here, weird, pier

Try saying this vowel phoneme in the sample words:

/er/	fast**er**, g**a**zump, curr**a**nt, woll**e**n, circ**u**s
	Not to be confused with the phoneme /ur/, this phoneme is very similar to /u/ but is slightly different in some regions.

Consonant phonemes with sample words

/b/	bag, rub
/d/	dad, could
/f/	off, calf, fast, graph, tough
/g/	ghost, girl, bag
/h/	here, who
/j/	bridge, giraffe, huge, jet
/k/	kite, antique, cat, look, quiet, choir, sock, six (note that the sound made by the letter x is a blend of the phonemes /k/ and /s/)
/l/	leg, crawl, full
/m/	mug, climb, autumn
/n/	now, gnash, knight, sign, fun
/p/	peg, tap
/r/	run, wrote
/s/	cinema, goose, listen, psalm, scene, see, sword, yes, less
/t/	ten, sit, receipt
/v/	vest, love
/w/	wet
/wh/	when (regional)
/y/	yes
/z/	choose, was, zoo
/th/	the, with
/th/	thank, path
/ch/	cheer, such, match
/sh/	shop, rush, session, chute
/zh/	usual
/ng/	thing, think

For some phonemes you may dispute some of the examples that we have listed. This may be due to regional variations in pronunciation. Disputing the sounds is a positive step as it ensures that you are analysing them!

It is not necessary to teach the children all the graphemes for each phoneme but to be ready and aware when pupils suggest words to you to represent a particular sound. They are not wrong with their suggestions and should be praised for recognising the phoneme.
You can then show them how the words that they have suggested are written but that normally the particular sound is represented by a specific grapheme.

Andrew Brodie: Supporting Phonics & Spelling © A & C Black Publishers Ltd. 2006

	Words	Phoneme
Words that open with a simple vowel sound, ie vc and vcc words:	am at and	/a/
		/e/
	in is it	/i/
	of on	/o/
	up	/u/

cvc words that appear in the Reception word list:

	Words	Phoneme
	can cat dad	/a/
	get yes	/e/
	big	/i/
	dog was	/o/
	*(note that the middle letter is **a** but the phoneme is /o/)*	
	mum	/u/ or /o/

cv, ccv and cvv words that appear in the Reception word list:

	Words	Phoneme
	he me she the we see	/ee/
	go no	/oe/
	to you	/ue/
	my	/ie/
	*(here the letter **y** is acting as a vowel so we would consider this word to be a cv word.)*	

Other words from the list:

a	come	I	said
all	day	like	they
are	for	look	this
away	going	play	went

Phonemes

Consonants: /k/,/b/,/d/,/g/,/h/,/j/,/m/,/n/,/p/,/t/,/v/
Vowel: /a/

Target words
cat, hat, bag, dad,
man, van, jam, tap

Teacher's notes

Sheet 1a

- Photocopy this page, then help the child cut out the eight letter **a** tiles.

- Revise the phoneme /a/ with the child. Depending on your school's policy, you could encourage the child to repeat both the name of the letter and the sound that it makes, saying for example, 'This is letter **a** and it says /a/.' Pronounce the phoneme as it would sound when used in a word, without adding any additional sounds.

Sheet 1b

- When you feel the child is ready, look at sheet 1b together. Ask him/her to point to the letters at the top of the page and to tell you the sounds they make.

- Help the child stick each letter **a** tile in the appropriate place in each word. Look at each word together, encouraging the child to blend phonemes (sounds) to read the words.

- Now cover the words one at a time. Say the word that is covered and help the child to segment the word into phonemes so that s/he can write it. Ask the child to read the word back to you once they have written it.

- As an additional activity you could make up some oral sentences together using some of the words on the sheet and pointing to these words as you say them, e.g. *The cat had a big hat. The man gave my dad some jam.* Write down one of the sentences for the child to copy. Encourage him/her to write clearly, following the school's handwriting policy, and to start the sentence with a capital letter and to finish with a full stop.

Sheet 1c

- This sheet includes the eight focus words with the vowel **a**. It could be photocopied for display purposes but could also be used to provide extra practice in writing the words.

- There are three writing lines for each word, one for writing the word quite large and the other two for smaller writing practice. You could write each word on the first of the two smaller writing lines so that the child can copy your writing in the correct style used by your school.

- The words provide lots of opportunities for discussion. Help the child to hear the sounds that the letters make. Encourage him/her to notice that the letter **a** appears in each word and that it makes the /a/ sound. Ask the child to find the rhyming words and then any words from the list that have *no* rhyming partner.

- Other cvc words with vowel phoneme /a/ that you could use for matching or rhyming games: bad, bat, cab, can, cap, dab, dap, fan, fat, fax, gag, gap, gas, had, hag, ham, has, jab, lad, lag, lap, lax, mad, map, mat, nag, nap, pad, pan, pat, rag, ram, ran, rap, rat, sad, sag, sap, sat, tab, tad, tag, tan, tat, tax, vat, wag, wax, yap, zap.

LETTER TILES

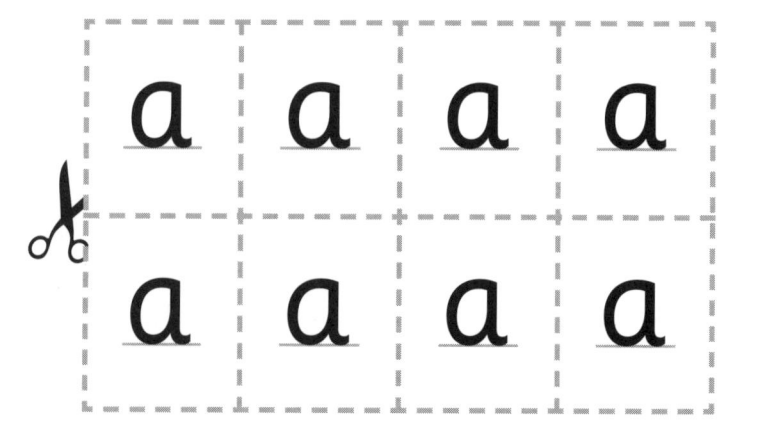

What sounds do the letters make?

c b d g h j m n p t v a

Stick the letter a in each word and say the word. Now copy each word.

c _ t

h _ t

b _ g

d _ d

m _ n

v _ n

j _ m

t _ p

Name: _____ **Date:** _____

Words for today

cat _____ _____

hat _____ _____

bag _____ _____

dad _____ _____

man _____ _____

van _____ _____

jam _____ _____

tap _____ _____

Learning objective	
Phonemes **Consonants:** /g/,/j/,/l/,/n/,/p/,/t/,/w/,/y/ **Vowel:** /e/	**Target words** leg, peg, get, jet, wet, net, yes, yet

Teacher's notes

Sheet 2a

- Photocopy this page, and then help the child cut out the eight letter **e** tiles.

- Revise the phoneme /e/ with the child. Depending on your school's policy, you could encourage the child to repeat both the name of the letter and the sound that it makes, saying for example, 'This is letter **e** and it says /e/.' Pronounce the phoneme as it would sound when used in a word, without adding any additional sounds.

Sheet 2b

- When you feel the child is ready, look at sheet 2b together. Ask him/her to point to the letters at the top of the page and to tell you the sounds they make.

- Help the child stick each letter **e** tile in the appropriate place in each word. Look at each word together, encouraging the child to blend phonemes (sounds) to read the words.

- Now cover the words one at a time. Say the word that is covered and help the child to segment the word into phonemes so that s/he can write it. Ask the child to read the word back to you once they have written it.

- As an additional activity you could make up some oral sentences together using some of the words and pointing to these words as you say them, e.g. *Do not get wet yet. Put the peg on the leg of the shorts.* Write down one of the sentences for the child to copy. Encourage him/her to write clearly, following the school's handwriting policy, and to start the sentence with a capital letter and to finish with a full stop.

Sheet 2c

- This sheet includes the eight focus words with the vowel **e**. It could be photocopied for display purposes but could also be used to provide extra practice in writing the words.

- There are three writing lines for each word, one for writing the word quite large and the other two for smaller writing practice. You could write each word on the first of the two smaller writing lines so that the child can copy your writing in the correct style used by your school.

- The words provide lots of opportunities for discussion. Help the child to hear the sounds that the letters make. Encourage him/her to notice that the letter **e** appears in each word and that it makes the /e/ sound. Ask the child to find the rhyming words and then any words from the list that have no rhyming partner.

- Other cvc words with vowel phoneme /e/ that you could use for matching or rhyming games: bed, beg, bet, den, fed, fen, fez, hem, hen, keg, ken, led, let, men, met, pen, pet, set, ten, vet, vex, web.

LETTER TILES

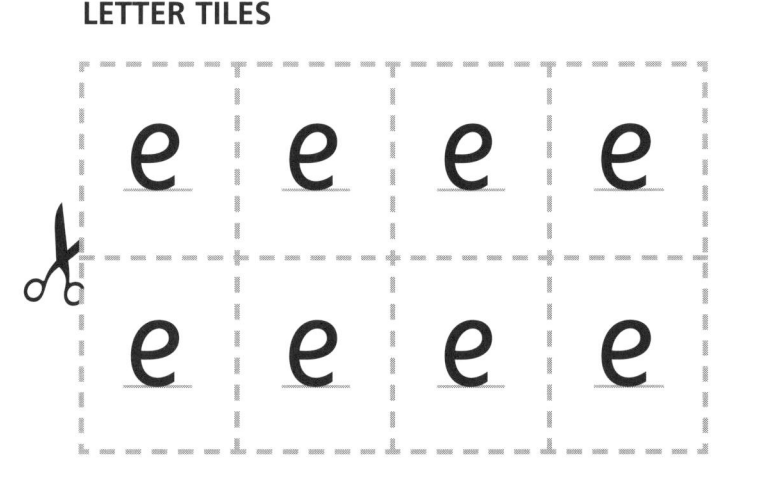

Andrew Brodie: Supporting Phonics & Spelling © A & C Black Publishers Ltd. 2006

Name: _____ **Date:** _____

What sounds do the letters make?

g j l n p t w y e

Stick the letter **e** in each word and say the word.
Now copy each word.

l __ g

_____

p __ g

_____

g __ t

_____

j __ t

_____

n __ t

_____

y __ s

_____

y __ t

_____

w __ t

_____

Andrew Brodie: Supporting Phonics & Spelling © A & C Black Publishers Ltd. 2006

yet

yes

net

wet

jet

get

peg

leg

Words for today

Name:

Date:

3a

Phonemes
Consonants: /b/,/d/,/h/,/k/,/m/,/n/,/p/,/s/,/t/,/z/
Vowel: /i/

Target words
bin, pin, kit, sit, his, hid, him, zip

Teacher's notes

Sheet 3a

- Photocopy this page and then help the child cut out the eight letter **i** tiles.

- Revise the phoneme /i/ with the child. Depending on your school's policy, you could encourage the child to repeat both the name of the letter and the sound that it makes, saying for example, 'This is letter **i** and it says /i/.' Pronounce the phoneme as it would sound when used in a word, without adding any additional sounds.

Sheet 3b

- When you feel the child is ready, look at sheet 3b together. Ask him/her to point to the letters at the top of the page and to tell you the sounds they make.

- Help the child stick each letter **i** tile in the appropriate place in each word. Look at each word together, encouraging the child to blend phonemes (sounds) to read the words.

- Now cover the words one at a time. Say the word that is covered and help the child to segment the word into phonemes so that s/he can write it. Ask the child to read the word back to you once they have written it.

- As an additional activity you could make up some oral sentences together using some of the words and pointing to these words as you say them, e.g. *Do not sit in the bin. He hid his PE kit.* Write down one of the sentences for the child to copy. Encourage him/her to write clearly, following the school's handwriting policy, and to start the sentence with a capital letter and to finish with a full stop.

Sheet 3c

- This sheet includes the eight focus words with the vowel **i**. It could be photocopied for display purposes but could also be used to provide extra practice in writing the words.

- There are three writing lines for each word, one for writing the word quite large and the other two for smaller writing practice. You could write each word on the first of the two smaller writing lines so that the child can copy your writing in the correct style used by your school.

- The words provide lots of opportunities for discussion. Help the child to hear the sounds that the letters make. Encourage him/her to notice that the letter **i** appears in each word and that it makes the /i/ sound. Ask the child to find the rhyming words and then any words from the list that have *no* rhyming partner.

- Other cvc words with vowel phoneme /i/ that you could use for matching or rhyming games: bib, bid, big, bit, did, dig, dim, din, dip, fib, fig, fin, fit, fix, gig, hip, hit, jib, jig, kid, kin, kip, lid, lip, lit, mix, nib, nip, nit, pig, pip, pit, rib, rid, rig, rim, rip, sin, sip, six, tin, tip, wig, win, wit, zit.

LETTER TILES

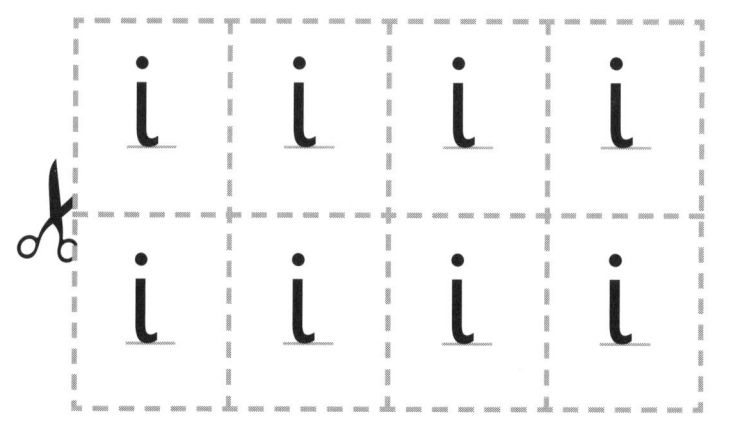

Name:

Date:

What sounds do the letters make?

b d h k m n p s t z i

Stick the letter **i** in each word and say the word.
Now copy each word.

b   n

p   n

k   t

s   t

h   s

h   d

h   m

z   p

Name: _____

Date: _____

Words for today

zip	
him	
hid	
his	
sit	
kit	
pin	
bin	

Andrew Brodie: Supporting Phonics & Spelling © A & C Black Publishers Ltd. 2006

4a

Learning objective

Phonemes
Consonants: /b/,/d/,/f/,/g/,/j/,/l/,/t/
Vowel: /o/

Target words
box, fox, dog, fog, jog, log, got, lot

Teacher's notes

Sheet 4a

- Photocopy this page, and then help the child cut out the eight letter **o** tiles.

- Revise the phoneme with the child. Depending on your school's policy, you could encourage the child to repeat both the name of the letter and the sound that it makes, saying for example, 'This is letter **o** and it says /o/.' Pronounce the phoneme as it would sound when used in a word, without adding any additional sounds.

Sheet 4b

- When you feel the child is ready, look at sheet 4b together. Ask him/her to point to the letters at the top of the page and to tell you the sounds they make.

- Help the child stick each letter **o** tile in the appropriate place in each word. Look at each word together, encouraging the child to blend phonemes (sounds) to read the words.

- Now cover the words one at a time. Say the word that is covered and help the child to segment the word into phonemes so that s/he can write it. Ask the child to read the word back to you once they have written it.

- As an additional activity you could make up some oral sentences together using some of the words and pointing to these words as you say them, e.g. *The fox sat on a box. The dog went for a jog and got lost in the fog.* Write down one of the sentences for the child to copy. Encourage him/her to write clearly, following the school's handwriting policy, and to start the sentence with a capital letter and to finish with a full stop.

Sheet 4c

- This sheet includes the eight focus words with the vowel **o**. It could be photocopied for display purposes but could also be used to provide extra practice in writing the words.

- There are three writing lines for each word, one for writing the word quite large and the other two for smaller writing practice. You could write each word on the first of the two smaller writing lines so that the child can copy your writing in the correct style used by your school.

- The words provide lots of opportunities for discussion. Help the child to hear the sounds that the letters make. Encourage him/her to notice that the letter **o** appears in each word and that it makes the /o/ sound. Ask the child to find the rhyming words and then any words from the list that have *no* rhyming partner.

- Other cvc words with vowel phoneme /o/ that you could use for matching or rhyming games: bog, bop, cob, cod, cog, cop, cot, cox, dot, god, hob, hod, hog, hop, hot, job, jot, lob, lop, mop, nod, not, pod, pop, pot, pox, rob, rod, rot, sob, sod, sop, top, tot, yon.

LETTER TILES

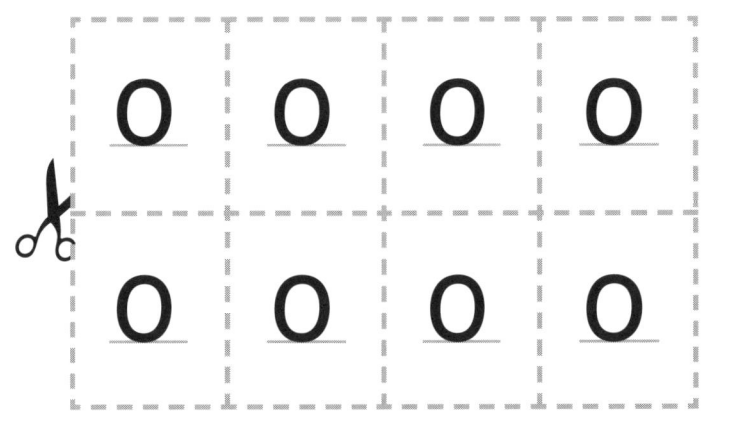

What sounds do the letters make?

b d f g j l t o

Stick the letter **o** in each word and say the word.
Now copy each word.

b ___ x

_____

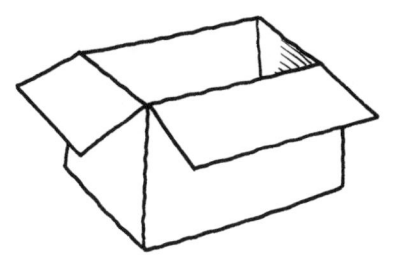

f ___ x

_____

d ___ g

_____

f ___ g

_____

j ___ g

_____

l ___ t

_____

l ___ g

_____

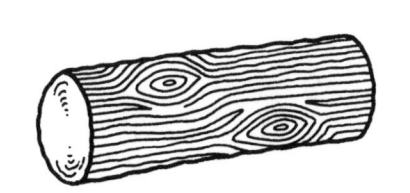

g ___ t

_____

Name: **Date:**

Words for today

box

fox

dog

jog

log

got

lot

Learning objective

5a **Phonemes** Consonants: /b/,/d/,/g/,/m/,/n/,/p/,/r/,/s/,/t/ Vowel: /u/	**Target words** mud, mug, mum, nut, fun, rub, rug, sun

Teacher's notes

Sheet 5a

- Photocopy this page, and then help the child cut out the eight letter **u** tiles.

- Revise the phoneme /u/ with the child. Depending on your school's policy, you could encourage the child to repeat both the name of the letter and the sound that it makes, saying for example, 'This is letter **u** and it says /u/.' Pronounce the phoneme as it would sound when used in a word, without adding any additional sounds.

Sheet 5b

- When you feel the child is ready, look at sheet 5b together. Ask him/her to point to the letters at the top of the page and to tell you the sounds they make.

- Help the child stick each letter **u** tile in the appropriate place in each word. Look at each word together, encouraging the child to blend phonemes (sounds) to read the words.

- Now cover the words one at a time. Say the word that is covered and help the child to segment the word into phonemes so that s/he can write it. Ask the child to read the word back to you once they have written it.

- As an additional activity you could make up some oral sentences together using some of the words and pointing to these words as you say them, e.g. *Mum sat on a rug in the sun. I had to rub my sore toe.* Write down one of the sentences for the child to copy. Encourage him/her to write clearly, following the school's handwriting policy, and to start the sentence with a capital letter and to finish with a full stop.

Sheet 5c

- This sheet includes the eight focus words with the vowel **u**. It could be photocopied for display purposes but could also be used to provide extra practice in writing the words.

- There are three writing lines for each word, one for writing the word quite large and the other two for smaller writing practice. You could write each word on the first of the two smaller writing lines so that the child can copy your writing in the correct style used by your school.

- The words provide lots of opportunities for discussion. Help the child to hear the sounds that the letters make. Encourage him/her to notice that the letter **u** appears in each word and that it makes the /u/ sound.

- Ask the child to find the rhyming words and then any words from the list that have *no* rhyming partner.

- Other cvc words with vowel phoneme /u/ that you could use for matching or rhyming games: bud, bug, bun, bus, but, cub, cup, cut, dub, dud, dug, fun, gum, gun, gut, hub, hug, hum, hut, jug, jut, nun, pun, pup, rut, sud, sum, sup, tub, tug, tut.

LETTER TILES

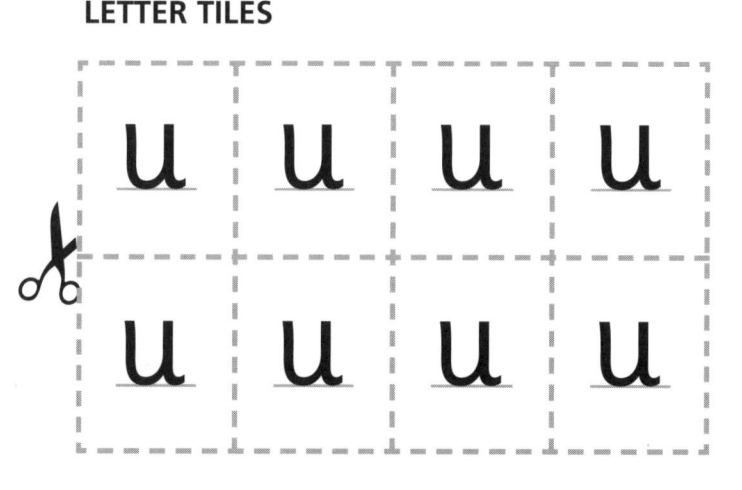

Name: **Date:**

What sounds do the letters make?

b d g m n p r s t u

Stick the letter **u** in each word and say the word.
Now copy each word.

m   d      m   g

_____   _____

m   m      n   t

_____   _____

f   n      r   g

_____   _____

r   b      s   n

_____   _____

Name: _____   **Date:** _____

Words for today

mud _____   _____

mug _____   _____

mum _____   _____

nut _____   _____

fun _____   _____

rub _____   _____

rug _____   _____

sun _____   _____

Andrew Brodie: Supporting Phonics & Spelling © A & C Black Publishers Ltd. 2006

6a

Learning objective

Phonemes
Consonants: /ch/,/m/,/n/,/p/,/r/,/s/,/t/
Vowels: /a/,/i/,/u/

Target words
chip, chin, chat, chum, chap, rich, such, much

Teacher's notes

Sheet 6a

- Photocopy this page, and then help the child cut out the eight tiles.
- Revise the phonemes with the child. Depending on your school's policy, you could encourage the child to repeat both the name of the letter and the sound that it makes, saying for example, 'This is letter **p** and it says /p/.' Pronounce the phoneme as it would sound when used in a word, without adding any additional sounds.

Sheet 6b

- When you feel the child is ready, look at sheet 6b together. Ask him/her to point to the letters at the top of the page and to tell you the sounds they make.
- Help the child stick each letter tile in the appropriate place in each word. Look at each word together, encouraging the child to blend phonemes (sounds) to read the words.
- Now cover the words one at a time. Say the word that is covered and help the child to segment the word into phonemes so that s/he can write it. Ask the child to read the word back to you once they have written it.
- As an additional activity you could make up some oral sentences together using some of the words and pointing to these words as you say them, e.g. *The rich man had a chat with a chum.*
- Write down one of the sentences for the child to copy. Encourage him/her to write clearly, following the school's handwriting policy, and to start the sentence with a capital letter and to finish with a full stop.

Sheet 6c

- This sheet includes the eight focus words with the consonant phoneme /ch/. It could be photocopied for display purposes but could also be used to provide extra practice in writing the words.
- There are three writing lines for each word, one for writing the word quite large and the other two for smaller writing practice. You could write each word on the first of the two smaller writing lines so that the child can copy your writing in the correct style used by your school.
- The words provide lots of opportunities for discussion. Help the child to hear the sounds that the letters make. Encourage him/her to notice that the phoneme /ch/ appears in each word sometimes at the beginning and sometimes at the end. The child might volunteer other words that also have the phoneme /ch/: cheese, cheer, chilly, cherry, chick, stitch.
- Ask the child to find the two words that rhyme.

LETTER TILES

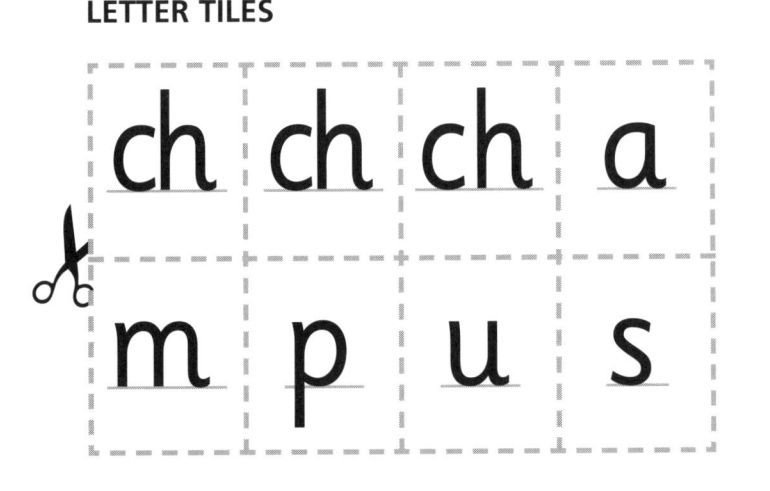

Name: **Date:**

What sounds do the letters make?

ch a i u m n p r s t

Stick a letter tile in each word and say the word.
Now copy each word.

in   ri

_____   _____

ch _ m   chi

_____   _____

ch _ t   uch

_____   _____

ap   uch

_____   _____

Andrew Brodie: Supporting Phonics & Spelling © A & C Black Publishers Ltd. 2006

Name: _____ **Date:** _____

Words for today

chip _____ _____

chin _____ _____

chat _____ _____

chum _____ _____

chap _____ _____

rich _____ _____

such _____ _____

much _____ _____

Learning objective

7a

Phonemes
Consonants: /sh/,/p/,/t/,/d/,/w/,/f/
Vowels: /i/,/o/,/u/,/ee/ (as in she)

Target words
she, shop, ship, shut, shed, wish, fish, dish

Teacher's notes

Sheet 7a

- Photocopy this page, and then help the child cut out the eight letter tiles.

- Revise the phonemes with the child. Depending on your school's policy, you could encourage the child to repeat both the name of the letter and the sound that it makes, saying for example, 'This is letter **w** and it says /w/.' Pronounce the phoneme as it would sound when used in a word, without adding any additional sounds.

Sheet 7b

- When you feel the child is ready, look at sheet 7b together. Ask him/her to point to the letters at the top of the page and to tell you the sounds they make.

- Help the child stick each letter tile in the appropriate place in each word. Look at each word together, encouraging the child to blend phonemes (sounds) to read the words.

- Now cover the words one at a time. Say the word that is covered and help the child to segment the word into phonemes so that s/he can write it. Ask the child to read the word back to you once they have written it.

- As an additional activity you could make up some oral sentences together using some of the words and pointing to these words as you say them, e.g. *She shut the shed. She had a fish on a dish.*

- Write down one of the sentences for the child to copy. Encourage him/her to write clearly, following the school's handwriting policy, and to start the sentence with a capital letter and to finish with a full stop.

Sheet 7c

- This sheet includes the eight focus words with the consonant phoneme /sh/. It could be photocopied for display purposes but could also be used to provide extra practice in writing the words.

- There are three writing lines for each word, one for writing the word quite large and the other two for smaller writing practice. You could write each word on the first of the two smaller writing lines so that the child can copy your writing in the correct style used by your school.

- The words provide lots of opportunities for discussion. Help the child to hear the sounds that the letters make. Encourage him/her to notice that the phoneme /sh/ appears in each word sometimes at the beginning and sometimes at the end. The child might volunteer other words that also have the phoneme /sh: shy, shine, shell, shin, shout, shock shore, short, shall.

- Ask the child to find the three words that rhyme.

LETTER TILES

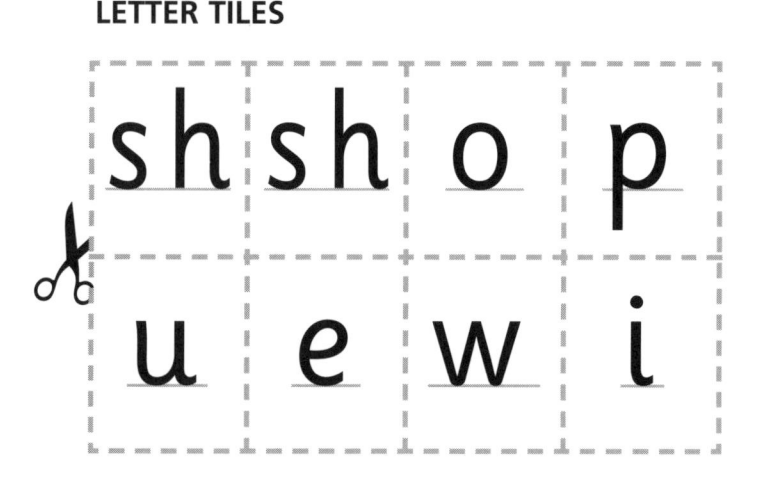

Andrew Brodie: Supporting Phonics & Spelling © A & C Black Publishers Ltd. 2006

Name: _____ **Date:** _____

What sounds do the letters make?

s h   e   i   o   p   u   w

Stick a letter tile in each word and say the word.
Now copy each word.

___ e   _____

s h ___ p   _____

s h i   _____

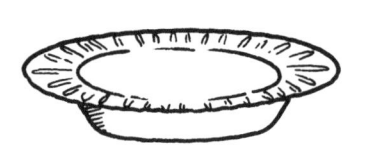

s h ___ t   _____

s h ___ d   _____

d ___ s h   _____

f i ___   _____

___ i s h   _____

Name: _____   **Date:** _____

Words for today

she _____ _____

shop _____ _____

ship _____ _____

shut _____ _____

shed _____ _____

wish _____ _____

fish _____ _____

dish _____ _____

8a

Learning objective

Phonemes
Consonants: /b/,/d/,/h/,/m/,/p/,/r/,/s/,/w/
Vowels: /ae/ (as in day)

Target words
bay, day, hay, may, pay, ray, say, way

Teacher's notes

Sheet 8a

- Photocopy this page, and then help the child cut out the eight letter tiles.

- Revise the phonemes with the child. Depending on your school's policy, you could encourage the child to repeat both the names of the letters and the sounds they make, saying for example, 'These are the letters **a** and **y** and together they can say /ae/.'

- Pronounce the phoneme as it would sound when used in a word, without adding any additional sounds.

Sheet 8b

- When you feel the child is ready, look at sheet 8b together. Ask him/her to point to the letters at the top of the page and to tell you the sounds they make.

- Help the child stick each letter tile in the appropriate place in each word. Look at each word together, encouraging the child to blend phonemes (sounds) to read the words.

- Now cover the words one at a time. Say the word that is covered and help the child to segment the word into phonemes so that s/he can write it. Ask the child to read the word back to you once they have written it.

- As an additional activity you could make up some oral sentences together using some of the words and pointing to these words as you say them, e.g. *I may go out today*.

- Write down one of the sentences for the child to copy. Encourage him/her to write clearly, following the school's handwriting policy, and to start the sentence with a capital letter and to finish with a full stop.

Sheet 8c

- This sheet includes the eight focus words with the consonant phoneme /ae/. It could be photocopied for display purposes but could also be used to provide extra practice in writing the words.

- There are three writing lines for each word, one for writing the word quite large and the other two for smaller writing practice. You could write each word on the first of the two smaller writing lines so that the child can copy your writing in the correct style used by your school.

- The words provide lots of opportunities for discussion. Help the child to hear the sounds that the letters make. Encourage him/her to notice that the phoneme /ae/ appears in each word, using the letters **a** and **y**. The child might volunteer other words that also have the phoneme /ae/: play, today, splay, spray, tray. He/she may make other suggestions for the phoneme /ae/. For example, the word *make* has the phoneme /ae/ in the form of a split digraph a_e; the word *rain* has the phoneme in the form of the grapheme **ai**. You should write the word that the child has suggested, giving appropriate praise for identifying the correct sound and showing him/her the way the sound appears in the word.

LETTER TILES

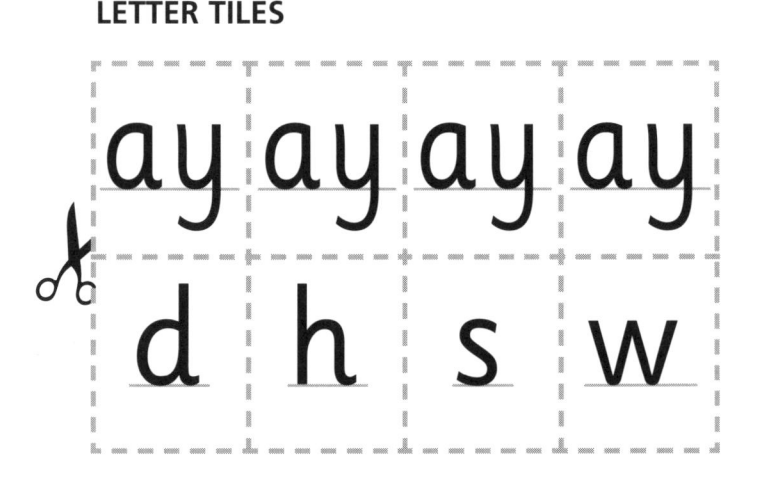

Name: _____   **Date:** _____

What sounds do the letters make?

a y   d   h   s   w   b   m   p   r

Stick a letter tile in each word and say the word.
Now copy each word.

b _____

ay

_____

_____

_____

ay

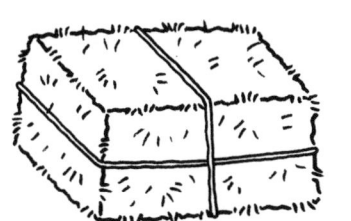

m _____

_____

_____

p _____

r _____

_____

_____

ay

ay

_____

_____

Name: _____   **Date:** _____

Words for today

bay _____ _____

day _____ _____

hay _____ _____

may _____ _____

pay _____ _____

ray _____ _____

say _____ _____

way _____ _____

9a

Learning objective

Phonemes
Consonants: /l/,/w/,/b/,/s/,/t/,/h/,/d/
Vowels: /e/,/i/,/o/

Target words
bell, doll, hill, ill, sell, tell, well, will

Teacher's notes

Sheet 9a

- Photocopy this page, and then help the child cut out the eight letter tiles.

- Revise the phonemes with the child. Depending on your school's policy, you could encourage the child to repeat both the names of the letters and the sounds they make, saying for example, 'This is the letter l; it sometimes works with another l and together they can say /l/ at the end of a word.'

- Pronounce the phoneme as it would sound when used in a word, without adding any additional sounds.

Sheet 9b

- When you feel the child is ready, look at sheet 9b together. Ask him/her to point to the letters at the top of the page and to tell you the sounds they make.

- Help the child stick each letter tile in the appropriate place in each word. Look at each word together, encouraging the child to blend phonemes (sounds) to read the words.

- Now cover the words one at a time. Say the word that is covered and help the child to segment the word into phonemes so that s/he can write it. Ask the child to read the word back to you once they have written it.

- As an additional activity you could make up some oral sentences together using some of the words and pointing to these words as you say them, e.g. *I will go out to play*.

- Write down one of the sentences for the child to copy. Encourage him/her to write clearly, following the school's handwriting policy, and to start the sentence with a capital letter and to finish with a full stop.

Sheet 9c

- This sheet includes the eight focus words with the consonant phoneme /l/ (spelled 'll'). This sheet could be copied for display purposes but can also be used to provide the child with extra practice in writing the words.

- There are three writing lines for each word, one for writing the word quite large and the other two for smaller writing practice. You could write each word on the first of the two smaller writing lines so that the child can copy your writing in the correct style used by your school.

- The words provide lots of opportunities for discussion. Help the child to hear the sounds that the letters make. Encourage him/her to notice that phoneme /l/ appears in each word. The child might volunteer other words that also have the phoneme /l/: spell, pull, till, mill, shell, shall, fill.

LETTER TILES

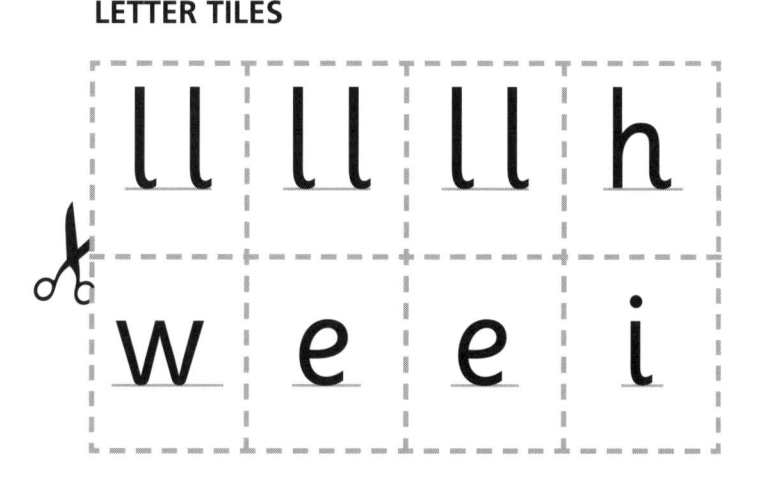

Andrew Brodie: Supporting Phonics & Spelling © A & C Black Publishers Ltd. 2006

Name: **Date:**

What sounds do the letters make?

ll   b   d   h   s   t   w

Stick a letter tile in each word and say the word.
Now copy each word.

b e ____   ____ ll

____   ____

e ll ____   w i ____

____   ____

i ll ____   s ____ ll

____   ____

d o ____   t ____ ll

____   ____

Name: _____ **Date:** _____

Words for today

bell _____ _____

doll _____ _____

hill _____ _____

ill _____ _____

sell _____ _____

tell _____ _____

well _____ _____

will _____ _____

Learning objective	
Phonemes Consonants: /b/,/d/,/j/,/l/,/m/,/n/,/v/,/s/,/t/ Vowels: /e/,/i/,/o/,/u/	**Target words** best, dust, just, list, lost, must, nest, vest

Teacher's notes

Sheet 10a

- Photocopy this page, and then help the child cut out the eight words.

- Revise the phonemes /s/ and /t/ with the child. Depending on your school's policy, you could encourage the child to repeat both the names of the letters and the sound they make in each of the words. It would be appropriate to focus on the final consonant blend by saying for example, 'These are the letters **s** and **t** and together they say 'st'.'

Sheet 10b

- When you feel the child is ready, look at sheet 10b together. Ask him/her to point to the letters at the top of the page and to tell you the sounds they make.

- Help the child stick the word tiles in the appropriate place in the sentences. Encourage him/her to say the words they have used.

- The child should then write each word and sentence in full and read it back to you once they have written it.

- Finally the child can read the four words they have not needed to stick on the sheet and suggest some simple sentences that include each of the words e.g. *The dog lost his bone.*

- You could ask the child to copy out one of the sentences. Encourage him/her to write clearly, following the school's handwriting policy, and to start the sentence with a capital letter and to finish with a full stop.

Sheet 10c

- This sheet includes the eight focus words with the consonant blend /s/ /t/ at the end of each one. It could be photocopied for display purposes but could also be used to provide extra practice in writing the words.

- There are three writing lines for each word, one for writing the word quite large and the other two for smaller writing practice. You could write each word on the first of the two smaller writing lines so that the child can copy your writing in the correct style used by your school.

- The words provide lots of opportunities for discussion. Help the child to hear the sounds that the letters make. Encourage him/her to notice that the blend /s/ /t/ appears in each word. The child might volunteer other words that also have the blend /s/ /t/: post, boast, roast, coast, last, fast, mist, rust.

WORD TILES

best dust just list

lost must nest vest

cheese
eggs
milk

Name: _____   **Date:** _____

What sounds do the letters make?

e i o u b d j l m n v

Choose the correct word tile to label each picture.

_____   _____

Choose the correct word tile to stick in each sentence. Copy the sentence.

I _____ go to the shops.

_____

I will write a shopping _____.

_____

Read the words that you still have. Tell your teacher some sentences that use the words you have.

Andrew Brodie: Supporting Phonics & Spelling © A & C Black Publishers Ltd. 2006

Name: _____ **Date:** _____

Words for today

best

dust

just

list

lost

must

nest

vest

Phonemes	**Target words**
Consonants: /b/,/h/,/l/,/m/,/p/,/s/,/n/,/d/ Vowels: /a/,/e/,/o/	and, hand, sand, bend, mend, send, lend, pond

Teacher's notes

Sheet 11a

- Photocopy this page, and then help the child cut out the eight letter tiles.

- Revise the phonemes with the child. Depending on your school's policy, you could encourage the child to repeat both the names of the letters and the sounds they make, saying for example, 'This is the letter **n** and it says /n/.'

Sheet 11b

- When you feel the child is ready, look at sheet 11b together. Ask him/her to point to the letters at the top of the page and to tell you the sounds they make.

- Help the child stick each letter tile in the appropriate place in each word. Look at each word together, encouraging the child to blend phonemes (sounds) to read the words.

- Now cover the words one at a time. Say the word that is covered and help the child to segment the word into phonemes so that s/he can write it. Ask the child to read the word back to you once they have written it.

- As an additional activity you could make up some oral sentences together using some of the words and pointing to these words as you say them, e.g. *Mend a toy and put it in my hand.*

- Write down one of the sentences for the child to copy. Encourage him/her to write clearly, following the school's handwriting policy, and to start the sentence with a capital letter and to finish with a full stop.

Sheet 11c

- This sheet includes the eight focus words with the consonant blend /n/ /d/. This sheet could be copied for display purposes but can also be used to provide the child with extra practice in writing the words.

- There are three writing lines for each word, one for writing the word quite large and the other two for smaller writing practice. You could write each word on the first of the two smaller writing lines so that the child can copy your writing in the correct style used by your school.

- The words provide lots of opportunities for discussion. Help the child to hear the sounds that the letters make. Encourage him/her to notice that the consonant blend /n/ /d/ appears at the end of each word. The child might volunteer other words that also have the final 'nd': find, kind, mind, tend, rind, bond, fund.

LETTER TILES

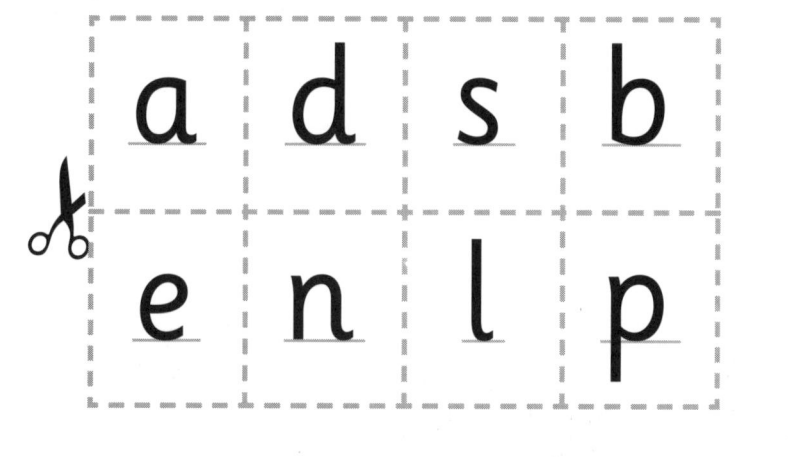

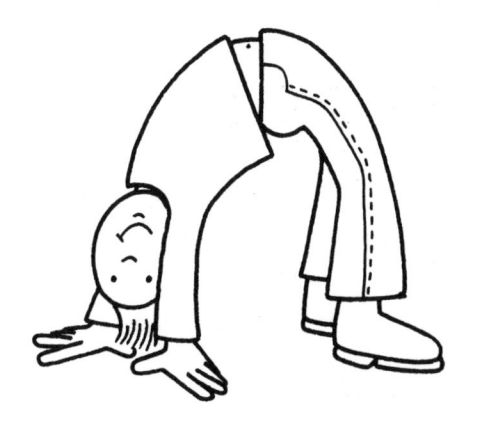

Name: _____ **Date:** _____

What sounds do the letters make?

a b d e h l m n o p s

Stick a letter tile in each word and say the word.
Now copy each word.

___ n d

h a n ___

_____

a n d

e n d

_____

m ___ n d

se ___ d

_____

___ o n d

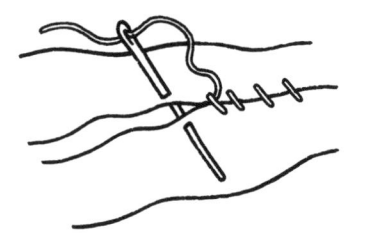

___ e n d

_____

11c

Name: _____ **Date:** _____

Words for today

and

hand

sand

bend

mend

send

lend

pond

12a

Learning objective	
Phonemes **Consonants:** /d/,/g/,/l/,/m/,/n/,/p/,/s/,/t/ **Vowels:** /a/,/ae/,/o/,/u/	**Target words** plum, play, plug, plus, plod, plop, plan, plot

Teacher's notes

Sheet 12a

- Photocopy this page, and then help the child cut out the eight words.
- Revise the phonemes /p/ and /l/ with the child. Depending on your school's policy, you could encourage the child to repeat both the names of the letters and the sound they make in each of the words. It would be appropriate to focus on the initial consonant blend by saying for example, 'These are the letters **p** and **l** and together they can say 'pl'.'

Sheet 12b

- When you feel the child is ready, look at sheet 12b together. Ask him/her to point to the letters at the top of the page and to tell you the sounds they make.
- Help the child stick the word tiles in the appropriate places in the sentences. Encourage him/her to say the words they have used.
- The child should then write each word in full and read it back to you once they have written it.
- Finally the child can read the four words they have not needed to stick on the sheet and suggest some simple sentences that include each of the words e.g. *I like to dig in the vegetable plot.*
- You could ask the child to copy out one of the sentences. Encourage him/her to write clearly, following the school's handwriting policy, and to start the sentence with a capital letter and to finish with a full stop.

Sheet 12c

- This sheet includes the eight focus words with the consonant blend /p//l/ at the beginning of each one. It could be photocopied for display purposes but could also be used to provide extra practice in writing the words.
- There are three writing lines for each word, one for writing the word quite large and the other two for smaller writing practice. You could write each word on the first of the two smaller writing lines so that the child can copy your writing in the correct style used by your school.
- The words provide lots of opportunities for discussion. Help the child to hear the sounds that the letters make. Encourage him/her to notice that the consonant blend /p/ /l/ appears in each word. The child might volunteer other words that also have the initial /p/ /l/ blend: plane, plate, plank, plant, plough, plenty, please, plimsoll. Some of these include quite complicated graphemes to represent certain phonemes: for example, ough for the phoneme /ow/. Discuss this with the child, although it may not be appropriate for him/her to learn this grapheme at this stage.

TARGET WORDS

plum play plug plus

plod plop plan plot

Name: _____ **Date:** _____

What sounds do the letters make?

ay p l g s d n t

Choose the correct word tile to label each picture.

_____   _____

Choose the correct word tile to stick in each sentence. Copy the sentence.

The boy ate a _____ .

_____

I like to _____ in the garden.

_____

Read the words that you still have. Tell your teacher some sentences that use the words you have.

Andrew Brodie: Supporting Phonics & Spelling © A & C Black Publishers Ltd. 2006

Andrew Brodie: Supporting Phonics & Spelling © A & C Black Publishers Ltd. 2006

12c

Name: _____ **Date:** _____

Words for today

plum

play

plug

plus

plod

plop

plan

plot

Learning objective

Phonemes
Consonants: /ch/,/r/,/s/,/l/,/h/,/m/,/k/,/f/
Vowels: /e/,/i/,/o/,/u/

Target words
less, mess, hiss, kiss, moss, fuss, chess, cress

Teacher's notes

Sheet 13a

- Photocopy this page, and then help the child cut out the eight letter tiles.

- Revise the phonemes with the child. Depending on your school's policy, you could encourage the child to repeat both the names of the letters and the sounds they make, saying for example, 'These are the letters **c** and **h**. Together they can say /ch/.'

Sheet 13b

- When you feel the child is ready, look at sheet 13b together. Ask him/her to point to the letters at the top of the page and to tell you the sounds they make.

- Help the child stick the letter tiles in the appropriate places on the words. Encourage him/her to say the words that they have made.

- The child should then write each word in full and read it back to you once they have written it.

- As an additional activity you could make up some oral sentences together using some of the words and pointing to these words as you say them, e.g. *The man playing chess made a fuss and a mess.*

- Write down one of the sentences for the child to copy. Encourage him/her to write clearly, following the school's handwriting policy, and to start the sentence with a capital letter and to finish with a full stop.

Sheet 13c

- This sheet includes the eight focus words with the consonant phoneme /s/ in the form of ss. This sheet could be copied for display purposes but can also be used to provide the child with extra practice in writing the words.

- There are three writing lines for each word, one for writing the word quite large and the other two for smaller writing practice. You could write each word on the first of the two smaller writing lines so that the child can copy your writing in the correct style used by your school.

- The words provide lots of opportunities for discussion. Help the child to hear the sounds that the letters make. Encourage him/her to notice that the phoneme /s/ appears at the end of each word, and that in all the words the /s/ sound is made from a doubling of the letter 's'. The child might volunteer other words that also have the double 's' ending: press, pass, miss, express.

LETTER TILES

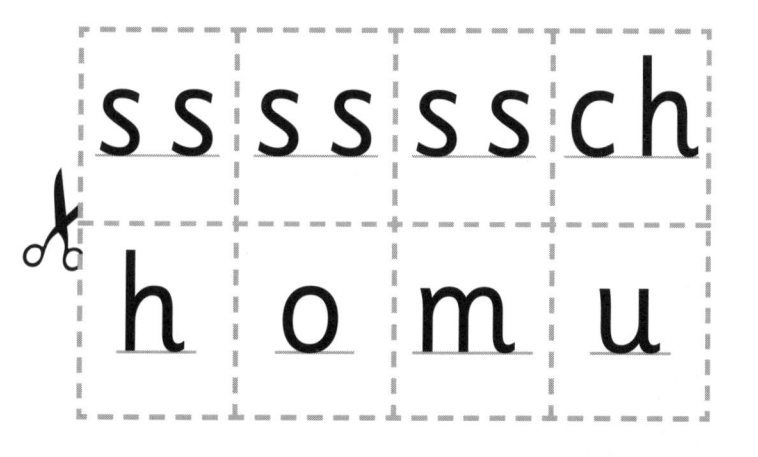

What sounds do the letters make?

ss ch c r f k m l h

Stick a letter tile in each word and say the word.
Now copy the words.

le _____      _____ ess

_____

iss      ki _____

m _____ ss      f _____ ss

e _____ ss   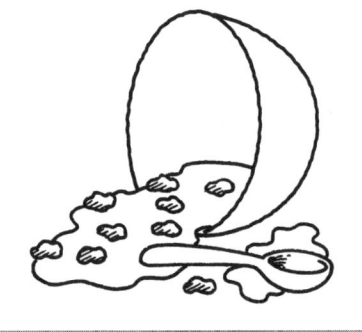   cre _____

13c

Name: **Date:**

Words for today

less _____

mess _____

hiss _____

kiss _____

moss _____

fuss _____

chess _____

cress _____

Andrew Brodie: Supporting Phonics & Spelling © A & C Black Publishers Ltd. 2006

14a

Learning objective

Phonemes
Consonants: /k/,/d/,/l/,/n/,/r/,/s/
Vowels: /a/,/e/,/i/,/o/,/u/

Target words
lock, neck, rock, sock, sack, lick, duck, kick

Teacher's notes

Sheet 14a

- Photocopy this page, and then help the child cut out the eight words.

- Revise the phoneme /k/ as the grapheme **ck** with the child. It would be appropriate to focus on the **ck** grapheme by saying: 'These are the letters c and k and together they say /k/.'

Sheet 14b

- When you feel the child is ready, look at sheet 14b together. Ask him/her to point to the letters at the top of the page and to tell you the sounds they make.

- Help the child stick the word tiles in the appropriate place in the sentences. Encourage him/her to say the words they have used.

- The child should then write each word in full and read it back to you once they have written it.

- As an additional activity you could make up some oral sentences together using some of the words and pointing to these words as you say them, e.g. *A duck stood on a rock*.

- You could ask the child to copy out one of the sentences. Encourage him/her to write clearly, following the school's handwriting policy, and to start the sentence with a capital letter and to finish with a full stop.

Sheet 14c

- This sheet includes the eight focus words with the grapheme **ck** at the end of each one. It could be photocopied for display purposes but could also be used to provide extra practice in writing the words.

- There are three writing lines for each word, one for writing the word quite large and the other two for smaller writing practice. You could write each word on the first of the two smaller writing lines so that the child can copy your writing in the correct style used by your school.

- The words provide lots of opportunities for discussion. Help the child to hear the sounds that the letters make. Encourage him/her to notice that the grapheme **ck** appears in each word. The child might volunteer other words that also end in **ck**: quick, quack, back, pack, (you could explain that the previous two words can be put together to form one word), tick, tack, trick, track, slick, sick.

TARGET WORDS

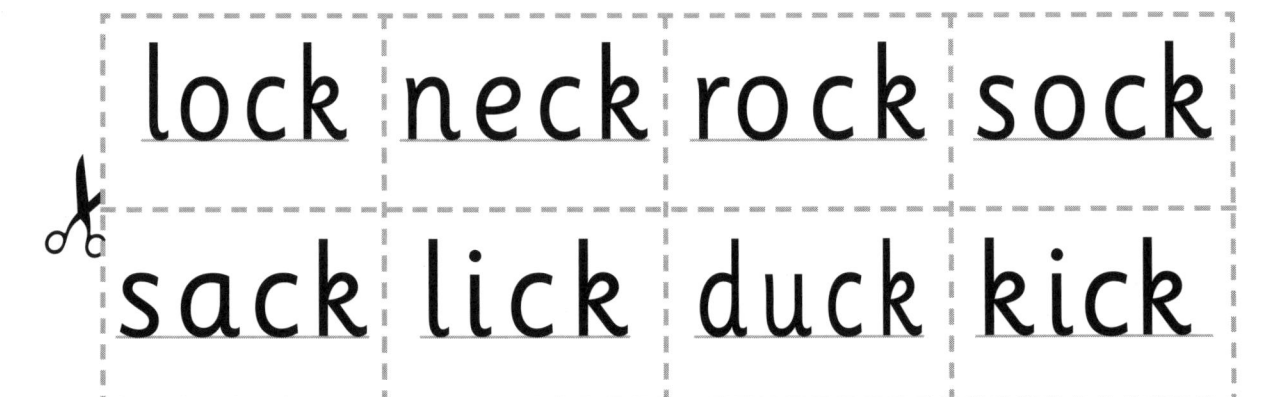

lock neck rock sock

sack lick duck kick

Name: **Date:**

What sounds do the letters make?

ck l n r s k d

Choose the correct word tile to label each picture.

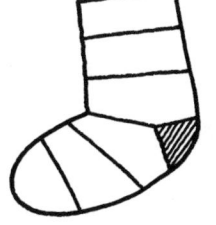

Name: _____

Date: _____

Words for today

lock _____ _____

neck _____ _____

rock _____ _____

sock _____ _____

sack _____ _____

lick _____ _____

duck _____ _____

kick _____ _____

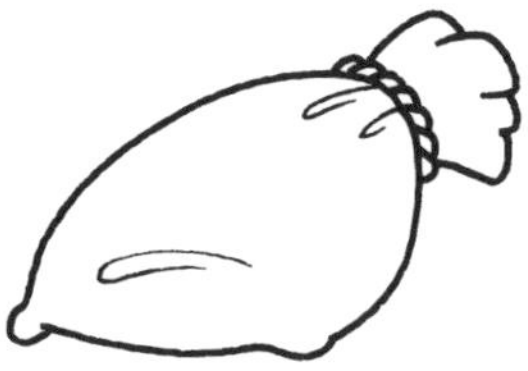

15a

Learning objective

Phonemes
Consonants: /ng/,/b/,/h/,/k/,/l/,/r/,/s/,/w/
Vowels: /a/,/i/,/o/,/u/

Target words
bang, hang, king, ring,
wing, song, long, rung

Teacher's notes

Sheet 15a

- Photocopy this page, and then help the child cut out the eight letter tiles.

- Revise the phonemes with the child. Depending on your school's policy, you could encourage the child to repeat both the names of the letters and the sounds they make, saying for example, 'These are the letters **n** and **g** and together they say /ng/'

Sheet 15b

- When you feel the child is ready, look at sheet 15b together. Ask him/her to point to the letters at the top of the page and to tell you the sounds they make.

- Help the child stick each letter tile in the appropriate place in each word. Look at each word together, encouraging the child to blend phonemes (sounds) to read the words.

- Now cover the words one at a time. Say the word that is covered and help the child to segment the word into phonemes so that s/he can write it. Ask the child to read the word back to you once they have written it.

- As an additional activity you could make up some oral sentences together using some of the words and pointing to these words as you say them, e.g. *The king sang a song. I hang my clothes up.*

- Write down one of the sentences for the child to copy. Encourage him/her to write clearly, following the school's handwriting policy, and to start the sentence with a capital letter and to finish with a full stop.

Sheet 15c

- This sheet includes the eight focus words with the consonant phoneme /ng/. This sheet could be copied for display purposes but can also be used to provide the child with extra practice in writing the words.

- There are three writing lines for each word, one for writing the word quite large and the other two for smaller writing practice. You could write each word on the first of the two smaller writing lines so that the child can copy your writing in the correct style used by your school.

- The words provide lots of opportunities for discussion. Help the child to hear the sounds that the letters make. Encourage him/her to notice that the phoneme /ng/ appears at the end of each word. The child might volunteer other words that also have the phoneme /ng/: sing, sung, rang, lung, fling, flung.

LETTER TILES

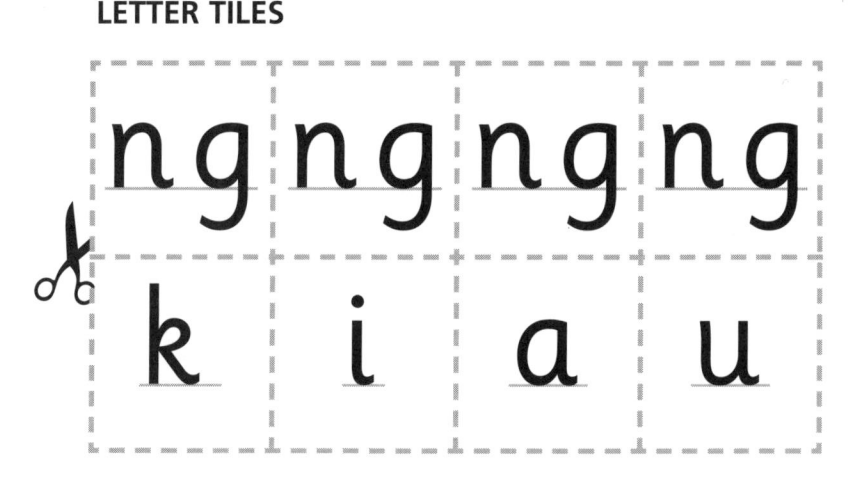

Name: _____ **Date:** _____

What sounds do the letters make?

ng a i o u k w s

Stick a letter tile in each word and say the word.
Now copy each word.

b a _____

_____ i n g

_____

w _____ n g

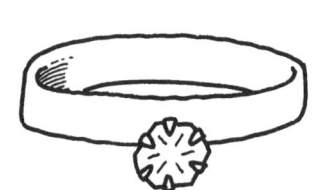

l o _____

_____

h _____ n g

r i _____

_____

s o _____

r _____ n g

_____

Name: _____   **Date:** _____

Words for today

bang _____   _____

hang _____   _____

king _____   _____

ring _____   _____

wing _____   _____

song _____   _____

long _____   _____

rung _____   _____

16a

Learning objective	**Target words**
Phonemes Consonants: /k/,/l/,/m/,/g/,/p/,/b/,/ng/ Vowels: /a/,/i/,/o/,/u/	clam, clog, clap, clock, click, clip, club, cling

Teacher's notes

Sheet 16a

- Photocopy this page, and then help the child cut out the eight words.

- Revise the phonemes with the child. Depending on your school's policy, you could encourage the child to repeat both the names of the letters and the sound they make in each of the words. It would be appropriate to focus on the initial consonant blend by saying: these are the letters **c** and **l** and together they can say 'cl'. You may also wish to point out to children that the letters 'c' and 'k' making the phoneme /k/, is revisited in two of the words on these sheets.

Sheet 16b

- When you feel the child is ready, look at sheet 16b together. Ask him/her to point to the letters at the top of the page and to tell you the sounds they make.

- Help the child stick the word tiles in the appropriate places in the sentences. Encourage him/her to say the words they have used. The child should then copy each sentence in full and read it back to you once they have written it.

- Finally the child can read the four words they have not needed and suggest some simple sentences that include each of these words e.g. *I go to a football club.*

- You could ask the child to copy out one of the sentences. Encourage him/her to write clearly, following the school's handwriting policy, and to start the sentence with a capital letter and to finish with a full stop.

Sheet 16c

- This sheet includes the eight focus words with the consonant blend /c/ /l/ at the beginning of each one. It could be photocopied for display purposes but could also be used to provide extra practice in writing the words.

- There are three writing lines for each word, one for writing the word quite large and the other two for smaller writing practice. You could write each word on the first of the two smaller writing lines so that the child can copy your writing in the correct style used by your school.

- The words provide lots of opportunities for discussion. Help the child to hear the sounds that the letters make. Encourage him/her to notice that the consonant blend /c/ /l/ appears in each word. The child might volunteer other words that also have the initial **cl** blend: class, claw, clutter, clang, cloud.

TARGET WORDS

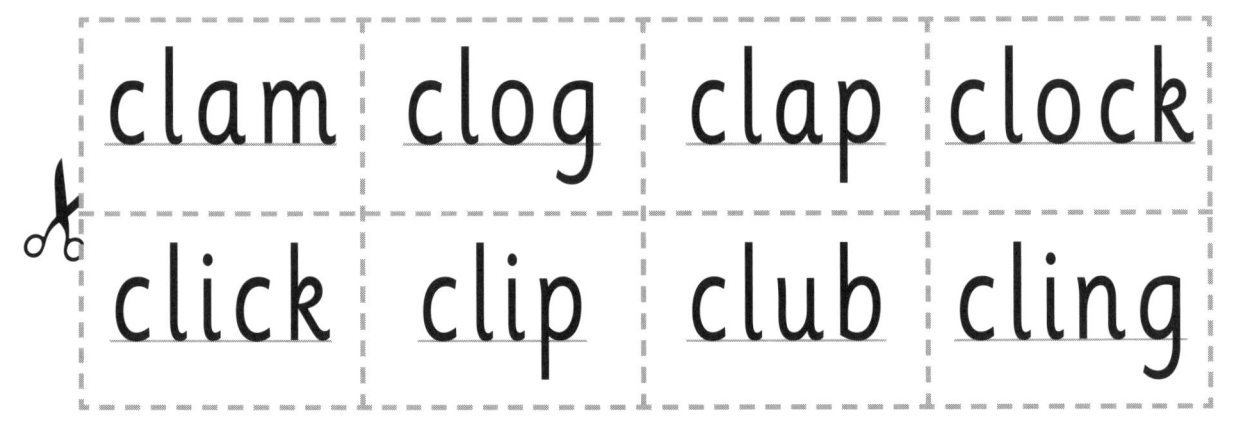

16b

Name: _____ **Date:** _____

What sounds do the letters make?

c l m p ck ng b g

Choose the correct word tile to label each picture.

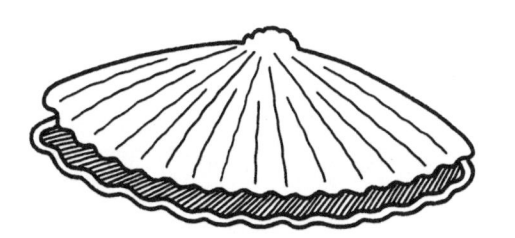 

_____ _____

Choose the correct word tile to stick in each sentence. Copy the sentence.

I can _____ my hands.

_____

Look at the _____ to see the time.

_____

Read the words that you still have. Tell your teacher some sentences that use the words you have.

Andrew Brodie: Supporting Phonics & Spelling © A & C Black Publishers Ltd. 2006

Name: **Date:**

Words for today

clam

clog

clap

clock

click

clip

club

cling

17a

Learning objective

Phonemes
Consonants: /s/,/k/,/m/,/d/,/t/,/r/
Vowels: /ar/,/e/,/i/,/u/

Target words
ask, mask, task, desk, disk, risk, tusk, dusk

Teacher's notes

Sheet 17a

- Photocopy this page, and then help the child cut out the eight letter tiles.

- Revise the phonemes with the child. Depending on your school's policy, you could encourage the child to repeat both the names of the letters and the sounds they make, saying for example, 'This is a letter **k** and it says /k/.' (Note that the letter **a** in the words on these sheets make an /ar/ sound or an /a/ sound, depending on regional accent.)

Sheet 17b

- When you feel the child is ready, look at sheet 17b together. Ask him/her to point to the letters at the top of the page and to tell you the sounds they make.

- Help the child stick each letter tile in the appropriate place in each word. Look at each word together, encouraging the child to blend phonemes (sounds) to read the words.

- Now cover the words one at a time. Say the word that is covered and help the child to segment the word into phonemes so that s/he can write it. Ask the child to read the word back to you once they have written it.

- As an additional activity you could make up some oral sentences together using some of the words and pointing to these words as you say them, e.g. *Ask to finish your task at the desk.*

- Write down one of the sentences for the child to copy. Encourage him/her to write clearly, following the school's handwriting policy, and to start the sentence with a capital letter and to finish with a full stop.

Sheet 17c

- This sheet includes the eight focus words with the consonant blend /s/ /k/. This sheet could be copied for display purposes but can also be used to provide the child with extra practice in writing the words.

- There are three writing lines for each word, one for writing the word quite large and the other two for smaller writing practice. You could write each word on the first of the two smaller writing lines so that the child can copy your writing in the correct style used by your school.

- The words provide lots of opportunities for discussion. Help the child to hear the sounds that the letters make. Encourage him/her to notice that the blend /s/ /k/ appears in each word at the end, but that there are also words with **sk** in other positions, e.g. *basket or ski.* The child might volunteer other words that also have the blend /s/ /k/: *flask, cask, skill, sketch.*

LETTER TILES

Name: _____ **Date:** _____

What sounds do the letters make?

a s m d e l r t u

Stick a letter tile in each word and say the word.
Now copy each word.

a s k

_____

_____

a

_____

_____

m   s k

_____

_____

d e s

_____

_____

i s k

_____

_____

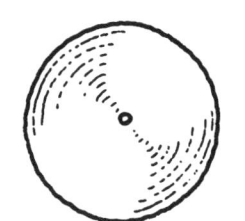

d i   k

_____

_____

t   s k

_____

_____

u s k

_____

_____

Name: _____ **Date:** _____

Words for today

ask _____ _____

mask _____ _____

task _____ _____

desk _____ _____

disk _____ _____

risk _____ _____

tusk _____ _____

dusk _____ _____

    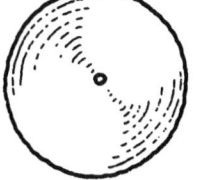

Learning objective

Phonemes
Consonants: /th/,/b/,/k/,/p/,/m/,/l/,/ng/
Vowels: /ar/ (or /a/ depending on regional accent) /i/,/o/

Target words
thin, thick, thing, cloth, path, moth, bath, both

Teacher's notes

Sheet 18a

- Photocopy this page, and then help the child cut out the eight letter tiles.
- Revise the phonemes with the child. Depending on your school's policy, you could encourage the child to repeat both the names of the letters and the sounds they make, saying for example, 'These are the letters 't' and 'h', and together they say /th/.' (All the words on these sheets use /th/ as in 'thin'.)

Sheet 18b

- When you feel the child is ready, look at sheet 18b together. Ask him/her to point to the letters at the top of the page and to tell you the sounds they make.
- Help the child stick the letter tiles in the appropriate places on the words. Encourage him/her to say the words that they have made.
- The child should then write each word in full and read it back to you once they have written it.
- As an additional activity you could make up some oral sentences together using some of the words and pointing to these words as you say them, e.g. *He went up a path. Do you like thin or thick bread?*
- Write down one of the sentences for the child to copy. Encourage him/her to write clearly, following the school's handwriting policy, and to start the sentence with a capital letter and to finish with a full stop.

Sheet 18c

- This sheet includes the eight focus words with the consonant phoneme /th/. This sheet could be copied for display purposes but can also be used to provide the child with extra practice in writing the words.
- There are three writing lines for each word, one for writing the word quite large and the other two for smaller writing practice. You could write each word on the first of the two smaller writing lines so that the child can copy your writing in the correct style used by your school.
- The words provide lots of opportunities for discussion. Help the child to hear the sounds that the letters make. Encourage him/her to notice that the phoneme /th/ appears in each word. The child might volunteer other words that also have the phoneme /th/: three, myth, maths, thimble, think, thunder, thousand, thump, thread. If s/he offers words such as 'there' and 'they' it provides an initial opportunity to discuss the fact that the /th/ phoneme can make the sound as heard in 'thin' or the slightly different sound heard in 'this'.

LETTER TILES

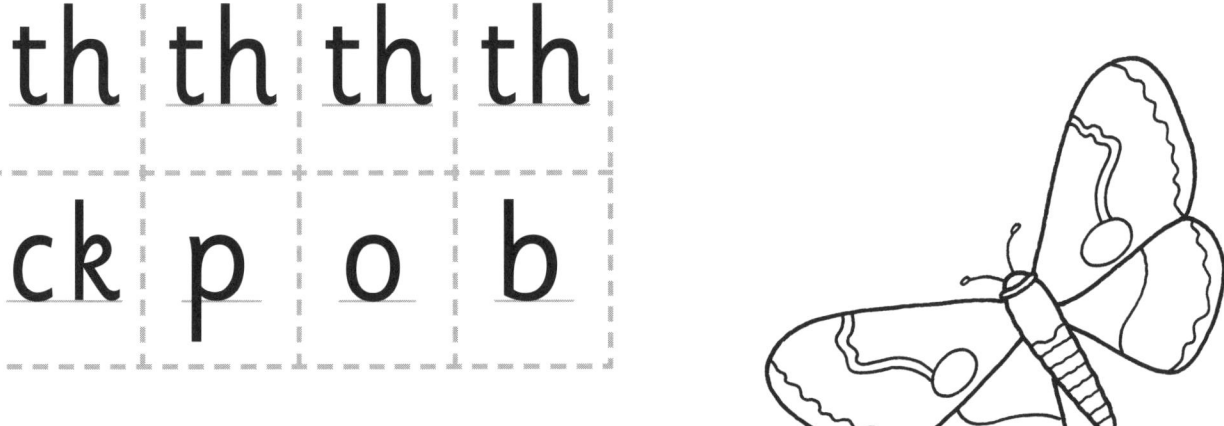
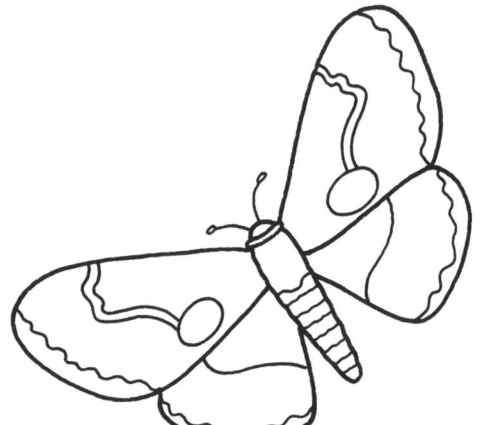

Name: _____ **Date:** _____

What sounds do the letters make?

th i n ng o p a m b

Stick a letter tile in each word and say the word.
Now copy each word.

thi _____   _____ in

_____   _____

ath _____   _____ ing

_____   _____

ba _____   m _____ th

_____   _____

clo _____   _____ oth

_____   _____

18c

Name: _____   **Date:** _____

Words for today

thin _____   _____

thick _____   _____

thing _____   _____

cloth _____   _____

path _____   _____

moth _____   _____

bath _____   _____

both _____   _____

Learning objective

Phonemes
Consonants: /th/,/s/,/t/,/n/,/m/
Vowels: /i/,/a/,/ae/,/ee/ or /u/ (The word *the* contains either the vowel phenome /u/ or /ee/ ~ this depends on whether the word *the* is followed by a word starting with a vowel or a consonant.)

Target words
the, this, that, then, than, them, they, with

Teacher's notes

Sheet 19a

- Photocopy this page, then help the child cut out the eight letter tiles.

- Revise the phonemes with the child. Depending on your school's policy, you could encourage the child to repeat both the names of the letters and the sounds they make, saying for example, 'These are the letters 't' and 'h', and together they say /th/.' All the words on these sheets use /th/ as in 'that'. It is important to discuss the spelling of the word 'they' with children as it is commonly misspelled 'thay'.

Sheet 19b

- When you feel the child is ready, look at sheet 19b together. Ask him/her to point to the letters at the top of the page and to tell you the sounds they make.

- Help the child stick each letter tile in the appropriate place in each word. Look at each word together, encouraging the child to blend phonemes (sounds) to read the words.

- Now cover the words one at a time. Say the word that is covered and help the child to segment the word into phonemes so that s/he can write it. Ask the child to read the word back to you once they have written it.

- As an additional activity you could make up some oral sentences together using some of the words and pointing to these words as you say them, e.g. *Do you like this one or that one? The girl went out with her mother.* Write down one of the sentences for the child to copy. Encourage him/her to write clearly, following the school's handwriting policy, and to start the sentence with a capital letter and to finish with a full stop.

Sheet 19c

- This sheet includes the eight focus words with the consonant phoneme /th/. This sheet could be copied for display purposes but can also be used to provide the child with extra practice in writing the words.

- There are three writing lines for each word, one for writing the word quite large and the other two for smaller writing practice. You could write each word on the first of the two smaller writing lines so that the child can copy your writing in the correct style used by your school.

- The words provide lots of opportunities for discussion. Help the child to hear the sounds that the letters make. Encourage him/her to notice that the phoneme /th/ appears in each word sometimes at the beginning and sometimes at the end. The child might volunteer other words that also have the phoneme /th/: thus, there, these, mother, father, brother.

LETTER TILES

Andrew Brodie: Supporting Phonics & Spelling © A & C Black Publishers Ltd. 2006

Name: **Date:**

What sounds do the letters make?

t h   s   i   t   a   n   m

Stick a letter tile in each word and say the word.
Now copy each word.

___ e ___   t h i ___

t h a ___   t h ___ n

t h ___ n   t h e ___

w i ___   ___ e y

Name: _____ **Date:** _____

Words for today

the	_____
this	_____
that	_____
then	_____
than	_____
them	_____
they	_____
with	_____

Andrew Brodie: Supporting Phonics & Spelling © A & C Black Publishers Ltd. 2006